Social Studies Alive!™

Our Community and Beyond

Interactive Student Notebook

Teachers' Curriculum Institute

Bert Bower   Jim Lobdell

Managing Editor: Laura M. Alavosus
Production Editor: Mali Apple
Editorial Assistant: Anna Embree
Art Director: Tim Stephenson
Production Coordinator: Lynn Sanchez
Senior Graphic Designer: Christy Uyeno
Graphic Designers: Katy Haun, Victoria Philp,
    Paul Rebello
Photographer: Tim Stephenson
Photo Acquisitions: Anna Embree
Audio and Photography Director: Katy Haun
Operations Manager: Ellen Mapstone

This book is published by Teachers' Curriculum Institute.

Teachers' Curriculum Institute
PO Box 50996
Palo Alto, CA 94303

Customer Service: 800-497-6138
www.teachtci.com

ISBN 1-58371-308-5
4 5 6 7 8 9 10 07 06

Program Directors

Bert Bower

Jim Lobdell

Program Author

Vicki LaBoskey, Professor of Education,

Mills College, Oakland, California

Ph.D., Curriculum and Teacher Education,

Stanford University, Stanford, California

Student Edition Authors

Laura M. Alavosus

John Bergez

Senior Curriculum Developer

Kelly Shafsky

Reading Specialist

Barbara Schubert, Reading Specialist,

Saint Mary's College, Moraga, California

Ph.D., Education, University of California,

Santa Barbara, California

Teacher Consultants

Judy Brodigan, Elementary Social Studies

Supervisor, Lewisville Independent

School District, Texas

Ann Dawson, Educational Consultant,

Intermediate Curriculum Specialist

Gahanna, Ohio

Candetta Holdren, Elementary Teacher,

Linlee Elementary, Lexington, Kentucky

Elizabeth McKenna, Elementary Teacher,

St. Thomas Aquinas Catholic School,

Diocese of Orlando, Florida

Lisa West, Instructional Specialist, Language Arts/

Social Studies, Landis Elementary School,

Houston, Texas

Beth Yankee, Elementary Teacher,

The Woodward School for Technology

and Research, Kalamazoo, Michigan

Internet and Literature Consultant

Debra Elsen, Elementary Teacher,

Manchester Elementary, Manchester Maryland

Music Specialist

Beth Yankee, Elementary Teacher,

The Woodward School for Technology

and Research, Kalamazoo, Michigan

Geography Specialist

David Knipfer

Mapping Specialists, Ltd.

Madison, Wisconsin

Contents

Part A

Label the equator, the prime meridian, and the four hemispheres on the maps below. Use your Interactive Student Deskmap to help you.

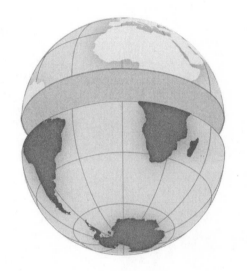

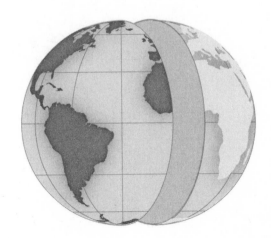

Part B

Label the four oceans and the seven continents on the map below. Use your Interactive Student Deskmap to help you.

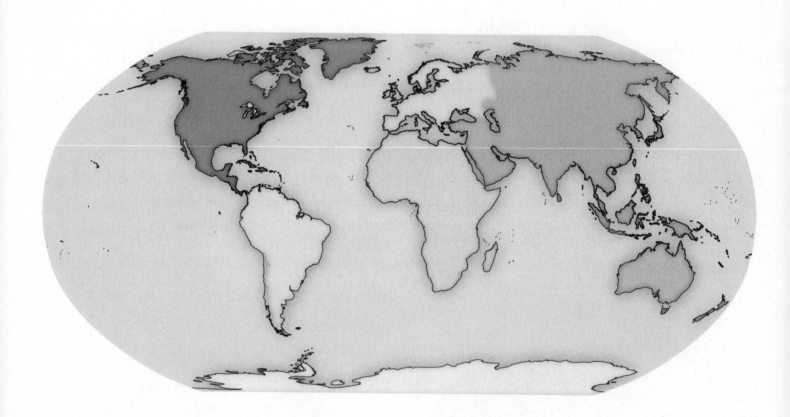

Part C

Label five countries on the map below. Use your Interactive Student Deskmap to help you.

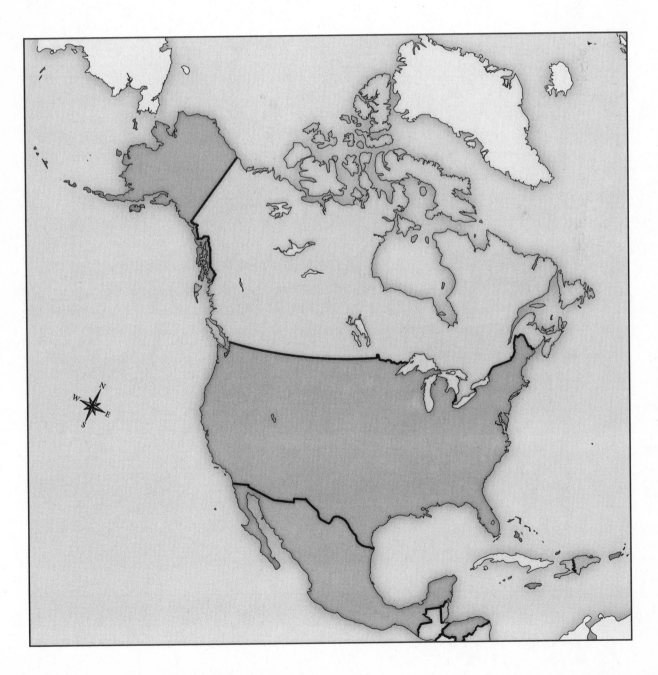

Part D

Label four states on the map below. Use your Interactive Student Deskmap to help you.

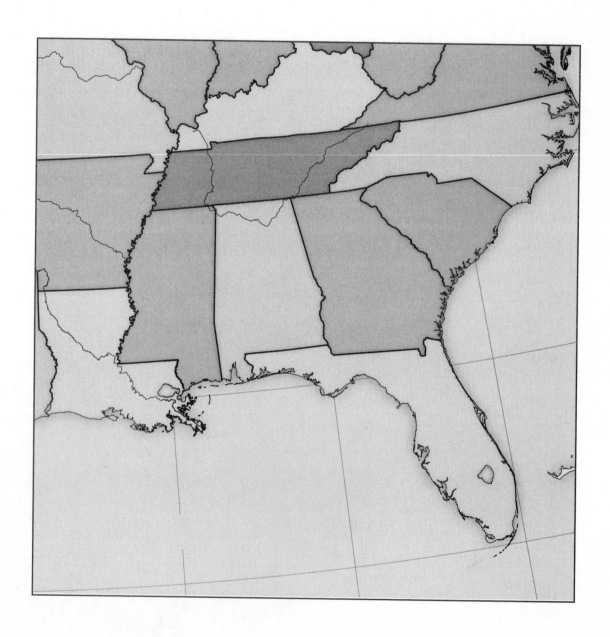

Part E

Label four communities on the map below. Use your
Interactive Student Deskmap to help you.

Your next mission is to land the space shuttle in your community. Use the maps below to identify the hemispheres, continent, country, state, and location of your community.

Part A: Hemispheres

- Look at the maps of the hemispheres.
- Find out in which hemispheres your community is located.
- Sketch a space shuttle on your hemispheres.

Write the names of the hemispheres here:

_____

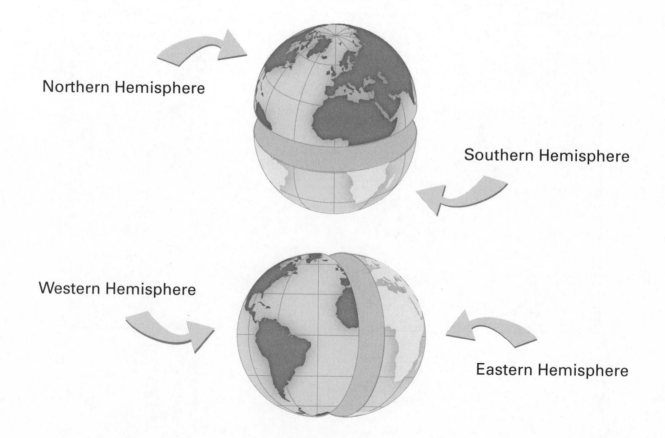

Part B: Continents

- Look at the map of the seven continents below.

- Find out on which continent your community is located.

- Sketch a space shuttle on that continent.

Write the name of the continent here:

_____

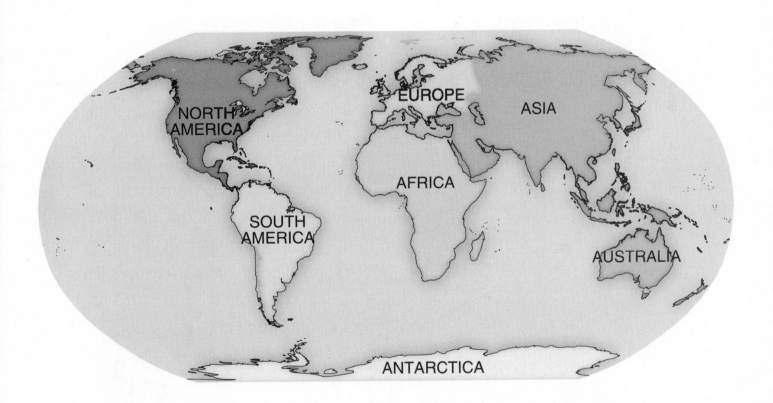

Part C: Countries

- Look at the map of the countries below.

- Find out in which country your community is located.

- Sketch a space shuttle on that country.

Write the name of the country here:

_____

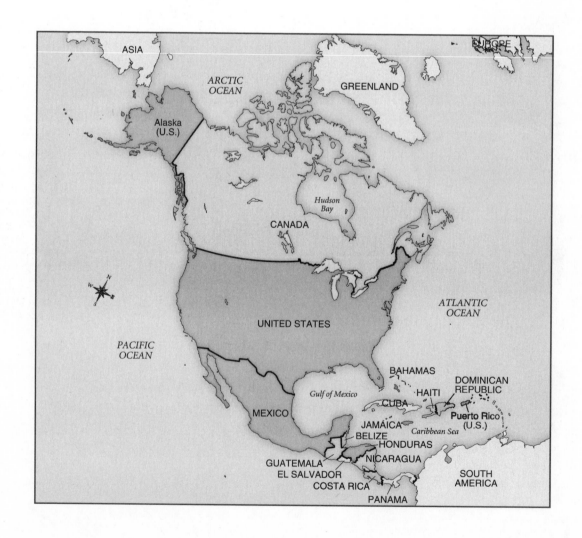

Part D: States

- Look at the map of the 50 states below.

- Find out in which state your community is located.

- Trace the outline of that state on the map.

- Sketch a space shuttle inside or near the outline of your state.

Write the name of the state here:

_____

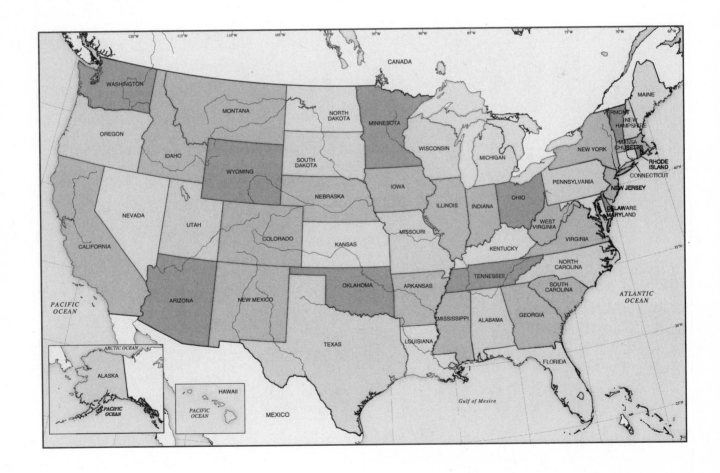

Part E: Communities

- Draw the outline of your state in the space below.
- Find out where in the state your community is located.
- Sketch a space shuttle in your state outline to show where your community is located.

Write the name of your community here:

_____

Where is the Statue of Liberty? Label the dot on the map with the name of the place and its state.

Draw a line between your community and the new place. Use your ruler to measure the distance between the two places. Write the distance on the line.

Complete the sentences below. Mark the direction on the compass rose.

The distance from _____

                                    (name of my community)

to the Statue of Liberty

is between _____ miles and _____ miles.

The direction from _____

                                    (name of my community)

to the Statue of Liberty is _____ .

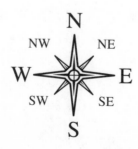

Where are the Everglades? Label the dot on the map with the name of the place and its state.

Draw a line between your community and the new place. Use your ruler to measure the distance between the two places. Write the distance on the line.

Complete the sentences below. Mark the direction on the compass rose.

The distance from _____

(name of my community)

to the Everglades

is between _____ miles and _____ miles.

The direction from _____

(name of my community)

to the Everglades is _____ .

Where is Mount Rushmore? Label the dot on the map with the name of the place and its state.

Draw a line between your community and the new place. Use your ruler to measure the distance between the two places. Write the distance on the line.

Complete the sentences below. Mark the direction on the compass rose.

The distance from _____

(name of my community)

to Mount Rushmore

is between _____ miles and _____ miles.

The direction from _____

(name of my community)

to Mount Rushmore is _____ .

Where is the Grand Canyon? Label the dot on the map with the name of the place and its state.

Draw a line between your community and the new place. Use your ruler to measure the distance between the two places. Write the distance on the line.

Complete the sentences below. Mark the direction on the compass rose.

The distance from _____

(name of my community)

to the Grand Canyon

is between _____ miles and _____ miles.

The direction from _____

(name of my community)

to the Grand Canyon is _____ .

Where is the Golden Gate Bridge? Label the dot on the map with the name of the place and its state.

Draw a line between your community and the new place. Use your ruler to measure the distance between the two places. Write the distance on the line.

Complete the sentences below. Mark the direction on the compass rose.

The distance from _____

(name of my community)

to the Golden Gate Bridge

is between _____ miles and _____ miles.

The direction from _____

(name of my community)

to the Golden Gate Bridge is _____ .

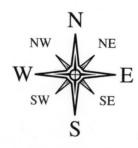

Look at the list of places below. Select one you would like to visit. Use resources in the classroom, library, or at home to find out where this place is in the United States. Which dot on the map is the place you chose?

- The White House, Washington, D.C.
- The Alamo, Texas
- Yellowstone National Park, Wyoming
- Hershey Chocolate Factory, Pennsylvania
- Disneyland, California

Now follow these directions:

1. Write the name of the place and the state you chose next to its dot on the map.
2. On the map, draw a straight line from your community to this new place.
3. Use your ruler to measure the distance between the two dots. Write the distance on the line.
4. Draw a line on the compass rose that shows which direction to travel from your community to the new place.

Fill in the chart.

Use the map and your book.

Name and Location of Community	Physical Geography *(examples: river, mountain)*	Natural Resources *(examples: wood, fish)*	Climate *(examples: temperature, weather)*
Roseburg, Oregon			
Las Cruces, New Mexico			
Gloucester, Massachusetts			

Step 1: Plan your travel brochure pages.

- Discuss the steps on each practice page with your partner.

- Write your ideas on the practice pages.

- Have your teacher check your work.

1. Write the name of the community and the state.

   _____

2. Draw an outline of the state. Place a dot where the community is located.

3. Write your names.

by _____

and _____

Physical geography of

_____

1. Write the name of the community on the line.

2. Draw or find a picture of one physical geographic feature in
   the community.

3. Write a sentence that describes the picture.

_____

_____

_____

Activity Notes 3

Natural resources of

____

1. Write the name of the community on the line.
2. Draw or find a picture of an important natural resource of the community.

3. Write a sentence that describes the picture.

____

____

____

Climate of

_____

1. Write the name of the community on the line.

2. Draw or find a picture of the climate of the community.

3. Write a sentence that describes the picture.

_____

_____

_____

Step 2: Complete your travel brochure.

- Fold a piece of construction paper in half to make four pages.

- Look at your ideas. Create your brochure.

- Is your brochure neat and colorful?

Complete the chart below for your own community.

My Community

Name _____

Location _____

Physical Geography (examples: river, mountain)	Natural Resources (examples: wood, fish)	Climate (examples: temperature, weather)

Make a travel brochure for your community.

Follow these steps:

- Write the name of your community and state.

- Draw an outline of the state. Put a dot where your community is in the state.

- Draw or paste a picture of one physical geographic feature of your community. Label it.

- Draw or paste a picture of one natural resource of your community. Label it.

- Draw or paste a picture of the climate of your community. Label it.

How is your community's geography like those you read about? How is the geography of your community different from those you read about? Write your answers below.

_____

_____

_____

_____

_____

_____

Draw a picture that shows you in a new place.

Were you happy? Sad? A little scared? Or mad?

Show how you felt.

Look at the faces below to help you.

Draw a line from each fact about immigrants to its match in the *Immigration Game*. (One fact does not have a match.)

Why Immigrants Come to the United States

Facts About Immigrants	The Immigration Game
• There were too many people in immigrants' countries.	• It was possible to earn more points in the large rectangle.
• There wasn't enough work or food in immigrants' countries.	• Several groups crowded into the small rectangle.
• There was war or unfair laws.	• There wasn't enough paper or crayons for everyone in the small rectangle.
• There was promise of gold or land in America.	

In the boxes, draw a simple picture to go with each
idea from the *Immigration Game*.

How Immigrants Get to the United States

Facts About Immigrants	The Immigration Game	
• Immigrants fill out papers and wait in lines for permission to go to America.	• Some students were sent back to the small rectangle.	
• Immigrants take long trips or walk to the United States.	• Students had to crawl to the large rectangle.	
• Immigrants pass tests to get into the United States.	• Students had to pass tests to get into the large rectangle.	
• Some immigrants were sent back.		

Draw a line from each fact to its match in the *Immigration Game*. (One fact does not have a match.) Draw a simple picture to go with each idea from the game.

Life for Immigrants in the United States

Facts About Immigrants	The Immigration Game
• Immigrants sometimes have to take low-paying or dangerous jobs.	• "Immigrant" groups earned 2 points for their drawings instead of 3.
• Immigrants are sometimes treated unfairly by others.	• "Immigrant" groups had more space and earned more points than before.
• Immigrants who work hard can make a better life.	• "Native" group took more paper and crayons and left less for "immigrant" groups.
• Some immigrants become famous or important leaders.	

Find out more about immigrants. Interview someone in your community who has immigrated to the United States. Or interview someone in your family about another person who immigrated to the United States.

Ask the questions below. Write the answers in the blank spaces.

Why did this person immigrate to the United States?

_____

_____

How did this person get to the United States?

_____

_____

What does this person like about living here?

_____

_____

What does this person not like about living here?

_____

_____

Brainstorm a list of foods from different cultures.
Don't forget foods from your family's culture. Try to
list examples that other groups might not.

_____	☐
_____	☐
_____	☐
_____	☐
_____	☐
_____	☐
_____	☐
_____	☐
_____	☐
_____	☐

Brainstorm a list of the names of languages that are spoken in communities around the United States. Try to list examples that other groups might not.

☐ _____

☐ _____

☐ _____

☐ _____

☐ _____

☐ _____

☐ _____

☐ _____

☐ _____

☐ _____

Brainstorm a list of holidays from different cultures that are celebrated in communities around the United States. Don't forget holidays from your family's culture. Try to list examples other groups might not.

_____ ☐

_____ ☐

_____ ☐

_____ ☐

_____ ☐

_____ ☐

_____ ☐

_____ ☐

_____ ☐

_____ ☐

Reading Notes 5

Brainstorm a list of traditions from different cultures that are followed in communities around the United States. Don't forget traditions from your family's culture. Try to list examples other groups might not.

☐ _____

☐ _____

☐ _____

☐ _____

☐ _____

☐ _____

☐ _____

☐ _____

☐ _____

☐ _____

Find or make an example of something that shows how a culture has contributed to your community. Bring the item to class. Here are a few categories to help you:

- Games
- Foods
- Clothes
- Arts
- Holidays

After you have made or selected an item, answer the questions below.

1. What is the name of the item?

_____

2. What culture contributed this item to your community?

_____

3. Explain something interesting about this item, such as how it is made or what it is used for.

_____

_____

_____

César Chávez

When was he born?

_____

What did he do to improve his community?

_____

_____

_____

How have his actions helped people in other communities?

_____

_____

_____

Ruby Bridges

When was she born?

_____

What did she do to improve her community?

_____

_____

_____

How have her actions helped people in other communities?

_____

_____

_____

Reading Notes 6

Lois Marie Gibbs

When was she born?

_____

What did she do to improve her community?

_____

_____

_____

How have her actions helped people in other communities?

_____

_____

_____

Judy Heumann

When was she born?

_____

What did she do to improve her community?

_____

_____

_____

How have her actions helped people in other communities?

_____

_____

_____

Steps for Creating a Human Statue

You group will create a human statue to celebrate the person you read about.

Step 1: Assign the four jobs.

To create the statue, the members of your group will take on four jobs: Speaker, Sculptor, Writer, and Geographer.

_____ will be the Speaker.

(name of group member)

_____ will be the Sculptor.

(name of group member)

_____ will be the Writer.

(name of group member)

_____ will be the Geographer.

(name of group member)

Teacher's initials _____

Step 2: Talk about what your statue will look like.

The Speaker leads a discussion about each person's role in the statue. The Speaker takes notes below.

Name of Group Member	Who This Student Represents	What This Student Will Do

Teacher's initials _____

Step 3: Create the statue.

The Sculptor leads a discussion on how the statue should look. The statue must show how the person made his or her community a better place to live.

The Sculptor leads the group in making a list of four props to use in the statue. The Sculptor assigns each person to bring one of the props.

1. _____ / _____
                (prop)   (person who will
                                               bring the prop)

2. _____ / _____
                (prop)   (person who will
                                               bring the prop)

3. _____ / _____
                (prop)   (person who will
                                               bring the prop)

4. _____ / _____
                (prop)   (person who will
                                               bring the prop)

The Sculptor then leads the group to practice getting in position for the statue.

Teacher's initials _____

Step 4: Write a plaque for the statue.

The Writer leads a discussion to write a sentence that will go on a plaque for the statue. The sentence should tell what the person did to improve his or her community.

The Writer writes a first draft of the sentence in the space below. The group checks that it is written neatly and that all words are spelled correctly.

Teacher's initials _____

Step 5: Decide where to put the statue.

The Geographer leads a discussion of where to put the statue. Below, write the name of the community you chose. Complete the sentence.

Name of community: _____

Our statue should go here because _____

_____

Your teacher will give you a map. The Geographer leads the group in finding the community you chose on that map. On the map below, draw a star to show where the community is located. Label the star with the community's name and the name of the person your statue represents.

Teacher's initials _____

Step 6: Prepare to present the statue.

The **Sculptor** makes sure the group members each bring a prop for the statue. The Sculptor has the group practice getting in position to make the statue and holding that position for two minutes. The Sculptor practices thanking the audience in a clear, loud voice.

The **Speaker** practices telling who each person in the statue represents and what he or she is doing. The Speaker talks in a clear, loud voice. The Speaker brings a prop for the statue.

The **Writer** neatly copies the plaque onto a new sheet of paper, in large letters and with all words spelled correctly. The Writer practices reading the plaque in a clear, loud voice. The Writer brings a prop for the statue.

The **Geographer** practices telling in which community the statue will be placed and why it will be placed there. The Geographer speaks in a loud, clear voice. The Geographer brings a prop for the statue.

Teacher's initials _____

Draw a picture of a statue that celebrates someone who made your community a better place to live. Below the statue, write a sentence on the plaque that explains what this person did to improve your community.

Talk with your partner about your homes and families. Listen for one or two things that are the same. Write them in the space where the two circles overlap.

What is different about your home and family compared to your partner's? Write one or two things that are different in the part of the diagram under the word "Me." Write one or two things that are different about your partner's home and family in the space under the words "My Partner."

Me   **My Partner**

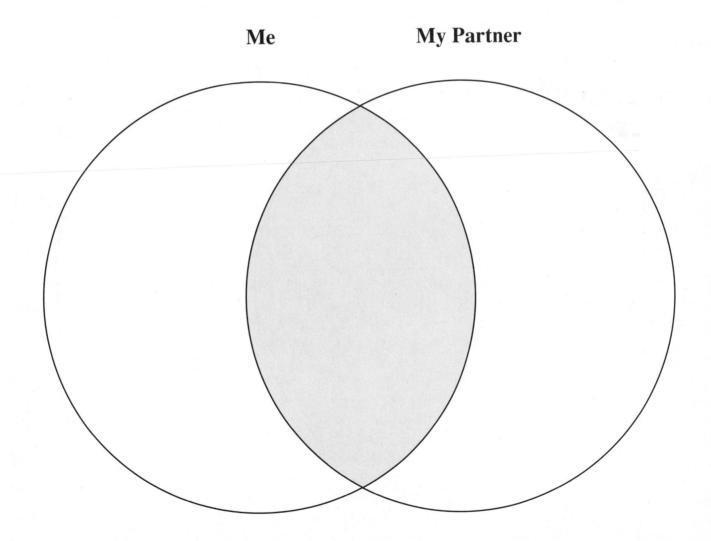

Read about Josie, and study her artifacts. Find one or two things about her home and family that are the same as yours. Write them where the circles overlap in the Venn diagram below.

What is different about her home and family compared to yours? Write one or two things that are different in each of the other two parts of the diagram.

Do the same thing to compare her school and her friends with yours.

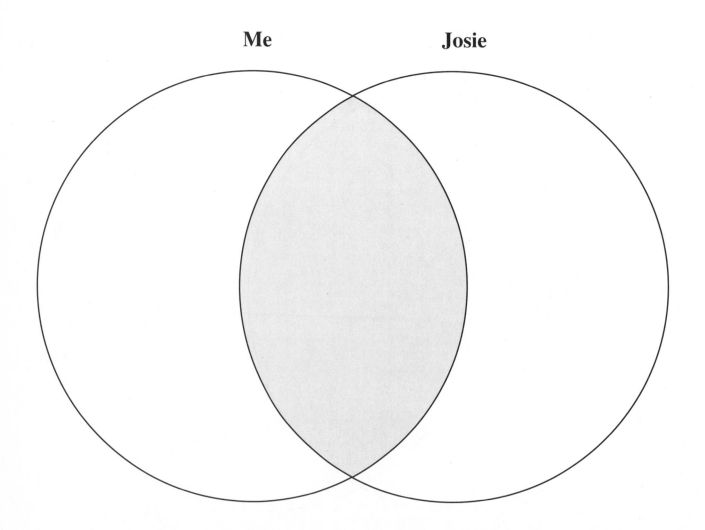

Me   Josie

Read about Luis, and study his artifacts. Find one or two things about his home and family that are the same as yours. Write them where the circles overlap in the Venn diagram below.

What is different about his home and family compared to yours? Write one or two things that are different in each of the other two parts of the diagram.

Do the same thing to compare his school and his friends with yours.

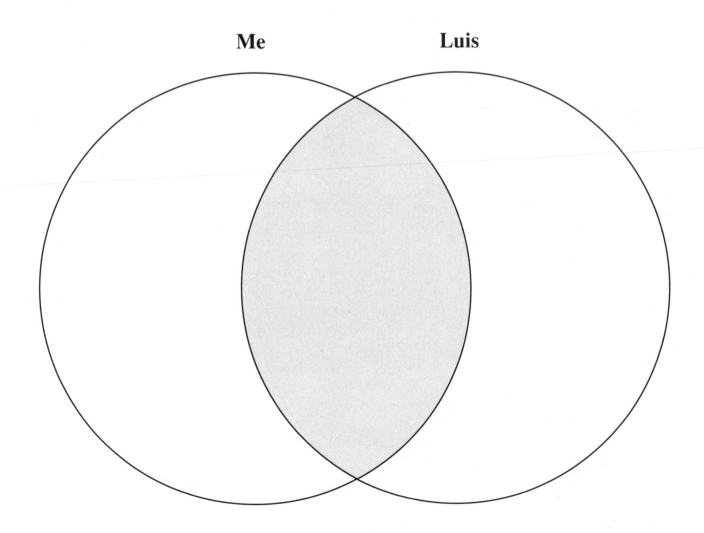

Me   **Luis**

Read about Kazuo, and study his artifacts. Find one or two things about his home and family that are the same as yours. Write them where the circles overlap in the Venn diagram below.

What is different about his home and family compared to yours? Write one or two things that are different in each of the other two parts of the diagram.

Do the same thing to compare his school and his friends with yours.

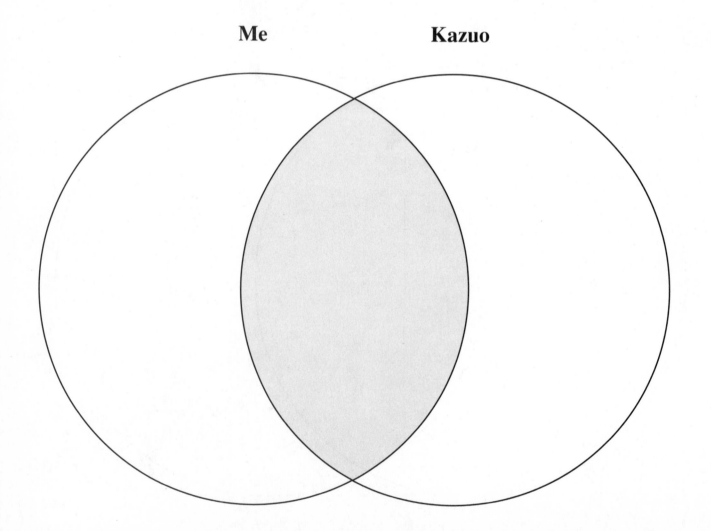

Me   **Kazuo**

Read about Emma, and study her artifacts. Find one or two things about her home and family that are the same as yours. Write them where the circles overlap in the Venn diagram below.

What is different about her home and family compared to yours? Write one or two things that are different in each of the other two parts of the diagram.

Do the same thing to compare her school and her friends with yours.

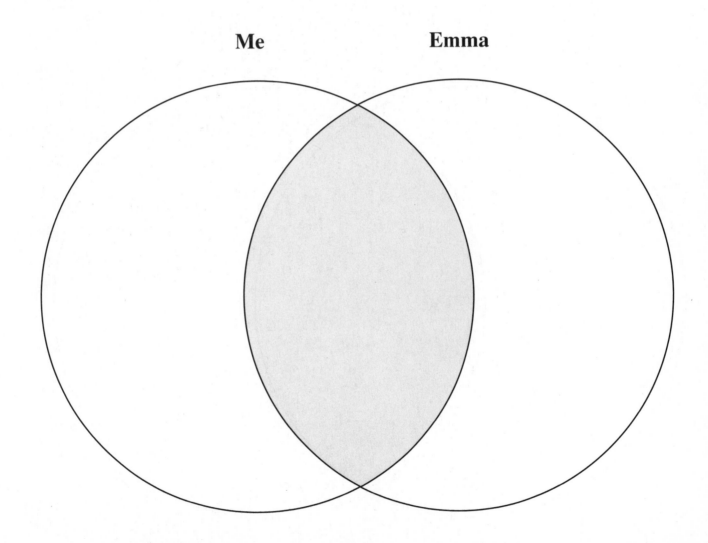

Me   **Emma**

Read about Paul, and study his artifacts. Find one or two things about his home and family that are the same as yours. Write them where the circles overlap in the Venn diagram below.

What is different about his home and family compared to yours? Write one or two things that are different in each of the other two parts of the diagram.

Do the same thing to compare his school and his friends with yours.

Me   **Paul**

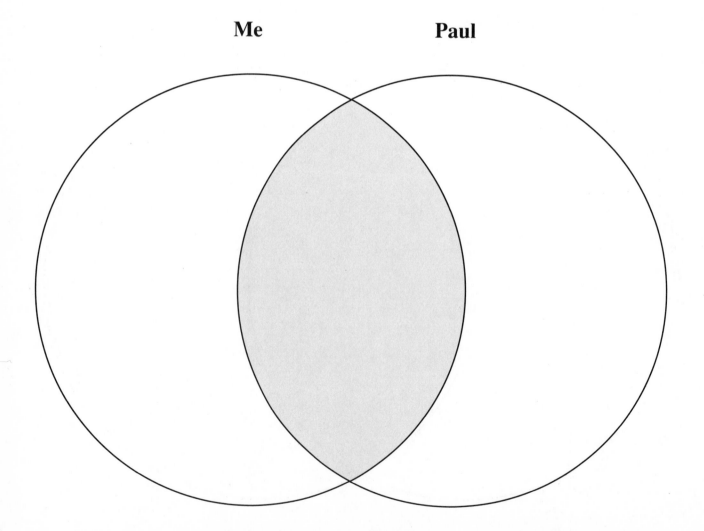

Read about Ana, and study her artifacts. Find one or two things about her home and family that are the same as yours. Write them where the circles overlap in the Venn diagram below.

What is different about her home and family compared to yours? Write one or two things that are different in each of the other two parts of the diagram.

Do the same thing to compare her school and her friends with yours.

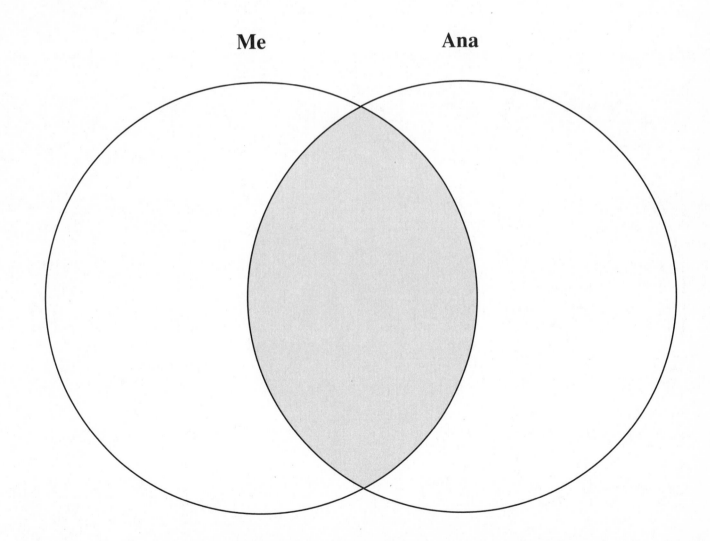

Me   **Ana**

Use your own words to complete the definitions below. Then, draw and label the buyer and the seller in the picture of the fruit market.

A market is

A buyer is

A seller is

Follow these steps to show what happens when supply is high and demand is low:

1. Label the buyer and seller in the picture.
2. In the thought bubbles, write what each is thinking when supply is high and demand is low.
3. Change the price on the sign to show what happens when supply is high and demand is low.

Follow these steps to show what happens when demand is high and supply is low:

1. Label the buyer and seller in the picture below.

2. Write what each is thinking when demand is high and supply is low.

3. Change the price on the sign to show what happens when demand is high and supply is low.

Find one item for each category. Look in newspaper ads, interview an adult, or go to a store with an adult.

High Supply and Low Demand = Low Price

Draw or paste a picture of the item here.

Why does this item have a low price?

_____

_____

_____

_____

_____

_____

_____

_____

PRICE

Then do the following:

- Draw or paste a picture of the item in the blank space.

- Write the price of the item on the price tag.

- Explain why you think the item has a low price or a high price.

Be sure to use the words "supply" and "demand" in your answer.

Low Supply and High Demand = High Price

Draw or paste a picture of the item here.

Why does this item have a high price?

_____

_____

_____

_____

_____

_____

_____

_____

PRICE

Read the assigned pages in your book. Then answer the question for that section. Glue one or two of the icons your teacher gives you in place of a word or phrase in your answer. One example is done for you.

Read pages 84 and 85, and answer this question:
Why do people in communities around the world trade things with each other? Use one icon in your answer.

Example:

People  with each other to get

things they don't have or can't make for themselves.

Read pages 84 and 85, and answer this question:

Why can communities trade things from all around the world today more than ever before? Use one icon in your answer.

_____

_____

_____

Read pages 86 and 87, and answer this question:

Why do some items come only from communities in certain parts of the world? Use one icon in your answer.

_____

_____

_____

Read pages 88 and 89, and answer this question:

What are two reasons people might buy items that are made only in certain parts of the world? Use two icons in your answer.

Read pages 90 and 91, and answer these questions:

What is one benefit of global trade? Use one icon in
your answer.

_____

_____

_____

What is one problem caused by global trade? Use one
icon in your answer.

_____

_____

_____

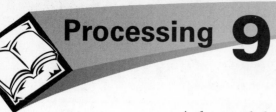

Ask an adult what things your community makes or grows that are traded to other parts of the world. Then follow these steps:

1. Sketch each item on the map at the right, near your community.

2. Label each sketch with the item's name.

3. Draw arrows from each sketch to at least two other parts of the world where you think the item is traded.

4. Select one of the items, and complete the sentences below the map. Fill in the blank, and circle the answer you think best explains why your community makes or grows the item.

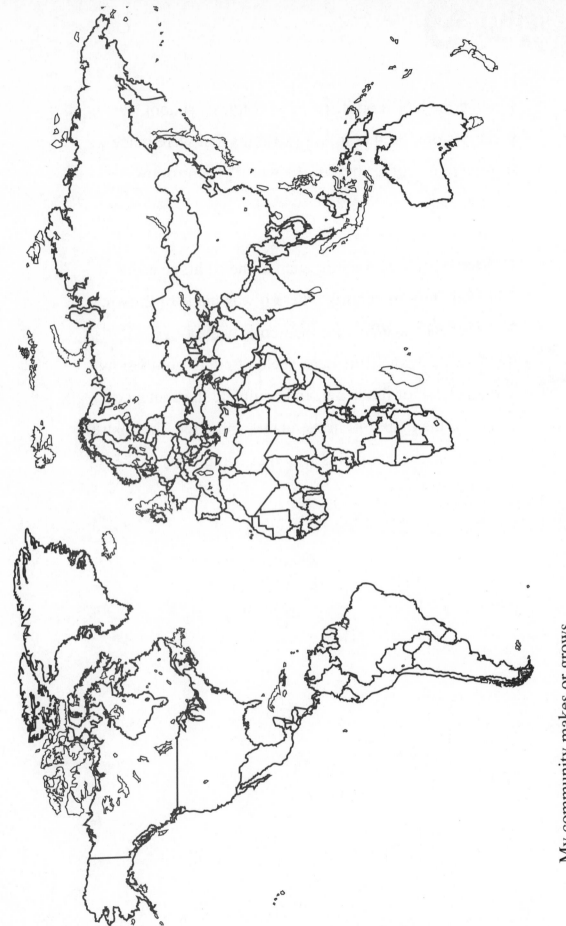

My community makes or grows _____.

I think we make or grow this item because

- my community is one of the few places where it can be grown or is found.

- my community is known for the quality of the items they make.

- my community produces the item for less money than other places do.

Look at the labels on items in your house, school, or grocery store. Find at least two things that were made or grown in another part of the world. Then follow these steps:

1. Sketch each item on the map at the right, near the community or country where it was made or grown.
2. Label each sketch with the item's name.
3. Draw an arrow from each sketch to your community.
4. Select one of the items, and complete the sentences below the map. Fill in the blank, and circle the answer you think best explains why that community makes or grows the item.

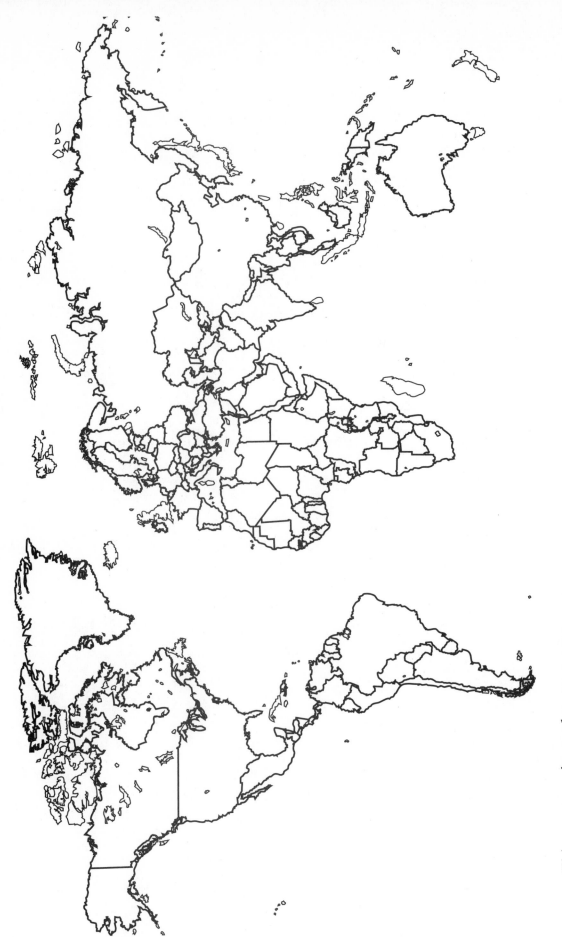

This community makes or grows _____ .

I think this community makes or grows this item because

- it is one of the few places where it can be grown or is found.

- it is known for the quality of the items made there.

- it produces the item for less money than other places do.

1. Think of the artifact your teacher showed you. What public service does it go with? Find the part of the drawing that matches this public service. Circle it.

2. Read the section of Chapter 10 about this public service. Then answer the questions below.

What is the name of the service? _____

How important is this public service?   (Circle one.)

not important   somewhat important   very important

Explain your answer.

_____

_____

_____

1. Look at the artifact. What public service does it go with? Find the part of the drawing that matches this public service. Circle it.

2. Read the section of Chapter 10 about this public service. Then answer the questions below.

What is the name of the service? _____

How important is this public service?   (Circle one.)

not important   somewhat important   very important

Explain your answer.

_____

_____

_____

1. Look at the artifact. What public service does it go with? Find the part of the drawing that matches this public service. Circle it.

2. Read the section of Chapter 10 about this public service. Then answer the questions below.

What is the name of the service? _____

How important is this public service?   (Circle one.)

not important   somewhat important   very important

Explain your answer.

_____

_____

_____

1. Look at the artifact. What public service does it go with? Find the part of the drawing that matches this public service. Circle it.

2. Read the section of Chapter 10 about this public service. Then answer the questions below.

What is the name of the service? _____

How important is this public service?   (Circle one.)

not important   somewhat important   very important

Explain your answer.

_____

_____

_____

1. Look at the artifact. What public service does it go with? Find the part of the drawing that matches this public service. Circle it.

2. Read the section of Chapter 10 about this public service. Then answer the questions below.

What is the name of the service? _____

How important is this public service?   (Circle one.)

not important somewhat important very important

Explain your answer.

_____

_____

_____

1. Look at the artifact. What public service does it go with? Find the part of the drawing that matches this public service. Circle it.

2. Read the section of Chapter 10 about this public service. Then answer the questions below.

What is the name of the service? _____

How important is this public service?   (Circle one.)

not important   somewhat important   very important

Explain your answer.

_____

_____

_____

Create a six-line acrostic poem below. Each line starts with one of the letters in the word PUBLIC. Each line should explain how one of the public services you learned about helps people in a community. At the end of each line, draw a simple symbol to represent that public service. The first line of the poem is done for you.

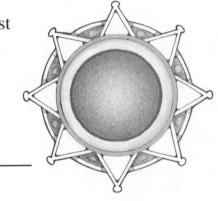

P olice make sure people in the community are safe. _____

U _____

B _____

L _____

I _____

C _____

1. Write the name of the person or department your teacher assigns to you on the line below.

2. Listen to the song your teacher plays.

3. With your partners, brainstorm ideas about what the person or department you were assigned might do. Use clues from the drawing and the song to help you. Write your ideas inside the outline of city hall below.

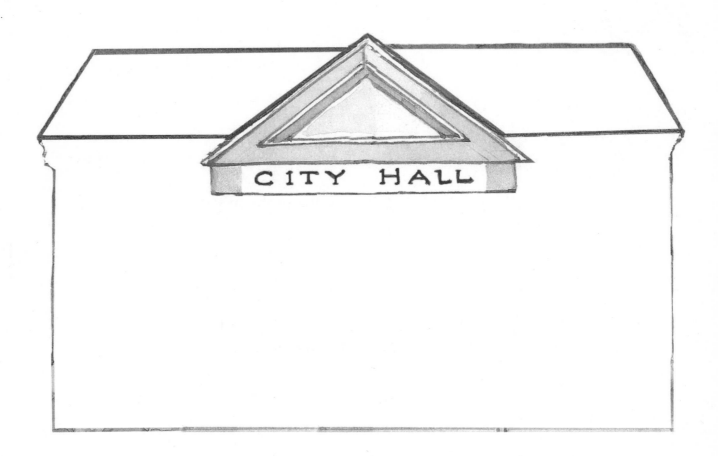

CITY HALL

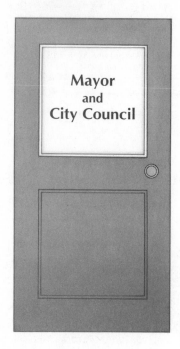

Mayor
and
City Council

Mayor and City Council

Pretend you work in this office. Write a short letter back to the author of the letter you read. Be sure to tell which person or department at city hall can help the writer of the letter, and explain why.

_____

Dear _____ ,

    I work in the _____ office.

We can help you with the problem you explained in your

letter because this office is responsible for _____

_____ .

This office is also responsible for _____

and _____ .

               Your public servant,

             _____

City Manager

Pretend you work in this office. Write a short letter back to the author of the letter you read. Be sure to tell which person or department at city hall can help the writer of the letter, and explain why.

City Manager

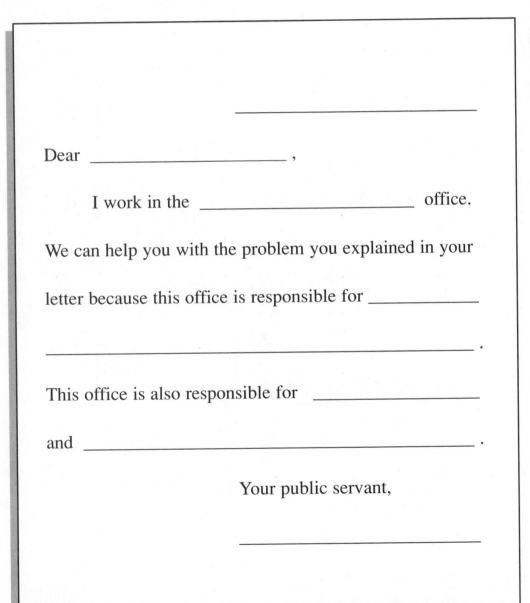

_____

Dear _____ ,

      I work in the _____ office.

We can help you with the problem you explained in your

letter because this office is responsible for _____

_____ .

This office is also responsible for _____

and _____ .

              Your public servant,

              _____

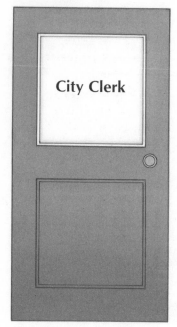

City Clerk

City Clerk

Pretend you work in this office. Write a short letter back to the author of the letter you read. Be sure to tell which person or department at city hall can help the writer of the letter, and explain why.

_____

Dear _____ ,

    I work in the _____ office.

We can help you with the problem you explained in your

letter because this office is responsible for _____

_____ .

This office is also responsible for _____

and _____ .

             Your public servant,

          _____

Parks and Recreation Department

Pretend you work in this office. Write a short letter back to the author of the letter you read. Be sure to tell which person or department at city hall can help the writer of the letter, and explain why.

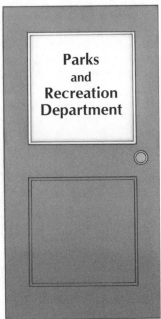

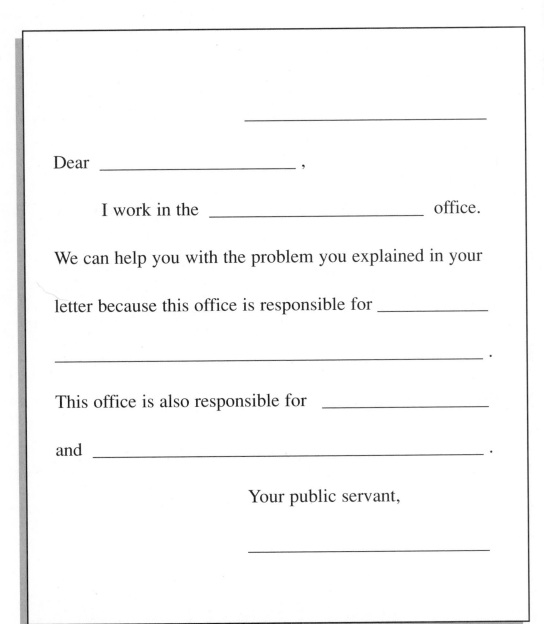

Dear _____ ,

I work in the _____ office.

We can help you with the problem you explained in your

letter because this office is responsible for _____

_____ .

This office is also responsible for _____

and _____ .

Your public servant,

_____

Public Library

Public Library

Pretend you work in this office. Write a short letter back to the author of the letter you read. Be sure to tell which person or department at city hall can help the writer of the letter, and explain why.

_____

Dear _____ ,

    I work in the _____ office.

We can help you with the problem you explained in your

letter because this office is responsible for _____

_____ .

This office is also responsible for _____

and _____ .

        Your public servant,

        _____

Fire Department

Pretend you work in this office. Write a short letter back to the author of the letter you read. Be sure to tell which person or department at city hall can help the writer of the letter, and explain why.

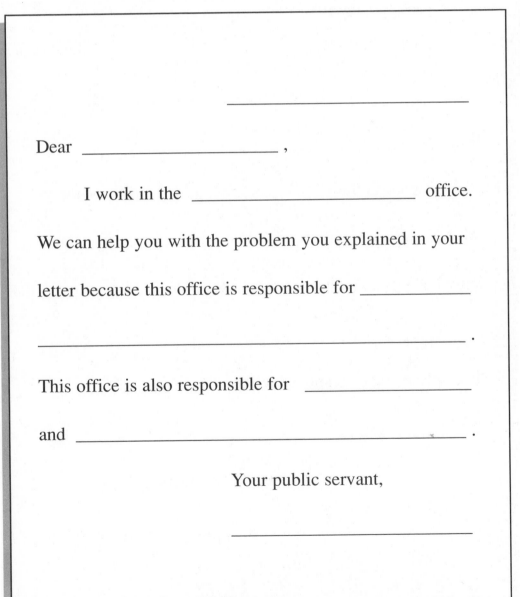

_____

Dear _____ ,

    I work in the _____ office.

We can help you with the problem you explained in your

letter because this office is responsible for _____

_____ .

This office is also responsible for _____

and _____ .

                    Your public servant,

              _____

Police Department

Police Department

Pretend you work in this office. Write a short letter back to the author of the letter you read. Be sure to tell which person or department at city hall can help the writer of the letter, and explain why.

_____

Dear _____ ,

      I work in the _____ office.

We can help you with the problem you explained in your

letter because this office is responsible for _____

_____ .

This office is also responsible for _____

and _____ .

                  Your public servant,

                  _____

Planning Department

Pretend you work in this office. Write a short letter back to the author of the letter you read. Be sure to tell which person or department at city hall can help the writer of the letter, and explain why.

Planning
Department

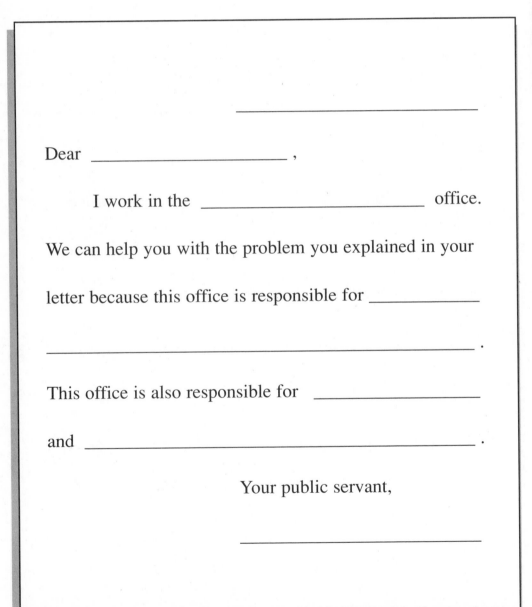

_____

Dear _____ ,

    I work in the _____ office.

We can help you with the problem you explained in your

letter because this office is responsible for _____

_____ .

This office is also responsible for _____

and _____ .

              Your public servant,

_____

Public
Works
Department

Public Works Department

Pretend you work in this office. Write a short letter back to the author of the letter you read. Be sure to tell which person or department at city hall can help the writer of the letter, and explain why.

_____

Dear _____ ,

    I work in the _____ office.

We can help you with the problem you explained in your

letter because this office is responsible for _____

_____ .

This office is also responsible for _____

and _____ .

                       Your public servant,

                _____

Complete this sentence:

Attending a public meeting gives people a voice in their

community because _____

_____

_____ .

Draw yourself in the picture. Then write what you would

say at a public meeting.

We should build a _____ in the

park because _____

_____

_____ .

Reading Notes 12

Complete this sentence:

Participating in a peaceful demonstration gives people a voice in their community because _____

_____ .

Draw your group in the picture. Then write what you would chant at a peaceful demonstration.

Complete this sentence:

Supporting a candidate gives people a voice in their

community because _____

_____.

Draw yourself in the crowd. Then write why you would

support one candidate.

I would support candidate _____

because _____

_____

_____.

Complete this sentence:

Voting gives people a voice in their community because

_____ .

Draw yourself in the picture. Then explain how you would vote.

I voted to build a _____ in the

park because _____

_____

_____ .

Select an important issue in your community or school. In the space below, design a poster to show how you feel about the issue. The poster should include a few simple drawings and a short slogan that is easy to remember.

Here are some issues you might consider:

- Should the community build a public skate park?
- Should gum be allowed in school?
- Should there be a school uniform?

In the outline of the Earth, write or draw what you think the word "environmental" means.

Create the first half of a Pollution Solution cartoon.
Follow the steps below.

1. Color the drawing below of the girls from El Segundo, California.

2. Fill in the speech bubble for each character to explain the problem the girls discovered.

Pollution

Create the second half of a Pollution Solution cartoon.

1. Draw one way the Tree Musketeers helped to solve the problem. Include the two characters from the first part of your cartoon.

2. Create a speech bubble for each character to explain how the Tree Musketeers helped to solve the problem.

Solution

Create the first half of a Pollution Solution cartoon.

1. Color the drawing below of the Exxon *Valdez* oil spill.
2. Fill in the speech bubbles for the two characters to explain what happened in the oil spill.

Pollution

Create the second half of a Pollution Solution cartoon.

1. Draw one way the communities affected by the oil spill helped to solve the problem. Include the characters from the first part of your cartoon.

2. Create a speech bubble for each character to explain how the communities helped to solve the problem.

Solution

Create the first half of a Pollution Solution cartoon.

1. Color the drawing below of a school yard.
2. Fill in the speech bubbles for the two characters to explain the problem they want to solve.

Pollution

Create the second half of a Pollution Solution cartoon.

1. Draw one way the community affected by the toxic waste site helped to solve the problem. Include the characters from the first part of your cartoon.

2 Create a speech bubble for each character to explain how the community helped to solve the problem.

Solution

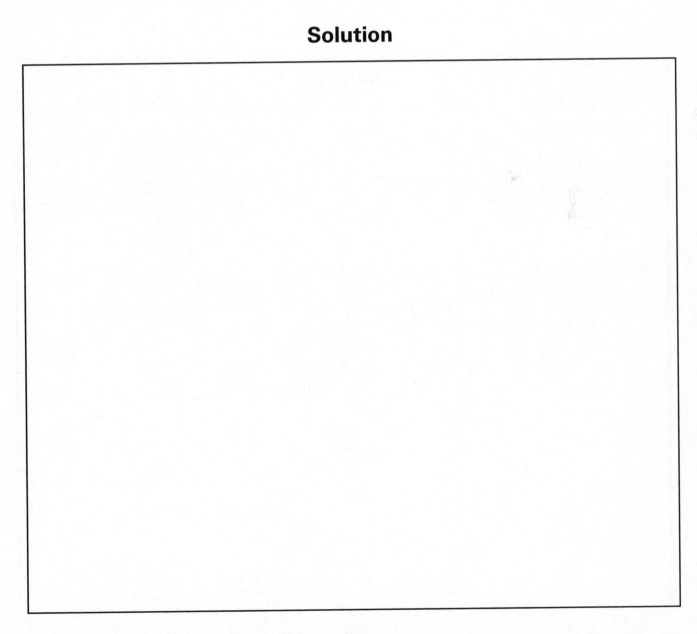

Create a Pollution Solution cartoon for your community.

1. Draw a picture of an environmental problem in your community. Include at least two characters in the drawing. (You can be one of them.)

2. Create a speech bubble for each character to explain the problem.

Pollution

Create the second half of your Pollution Solution cartoon.

1. Draw a picture to show what you think your community should do to solve the problem. Include the characters from the first drawing.

2. Create a speech bubble for each character to explain how the problem might be solved.

Solution

In the space below, design a bumper sticker about something you think is important and feel strongly about. Your bumper sticker should

- include three to five words.

- be colorful.

- have one simple picture or symbol.

As a group, carefully read pages 144–146 in your book. Find three examples of how people can protect the environment. For each idea, complete the sentence on the car. Then design a simple bumper sticker that someone who likes that idea might put on a car.

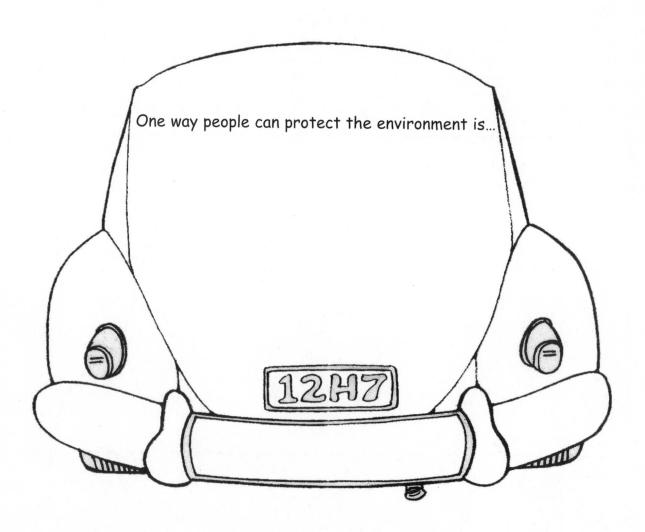

One way people can protect the environment is…

12H7

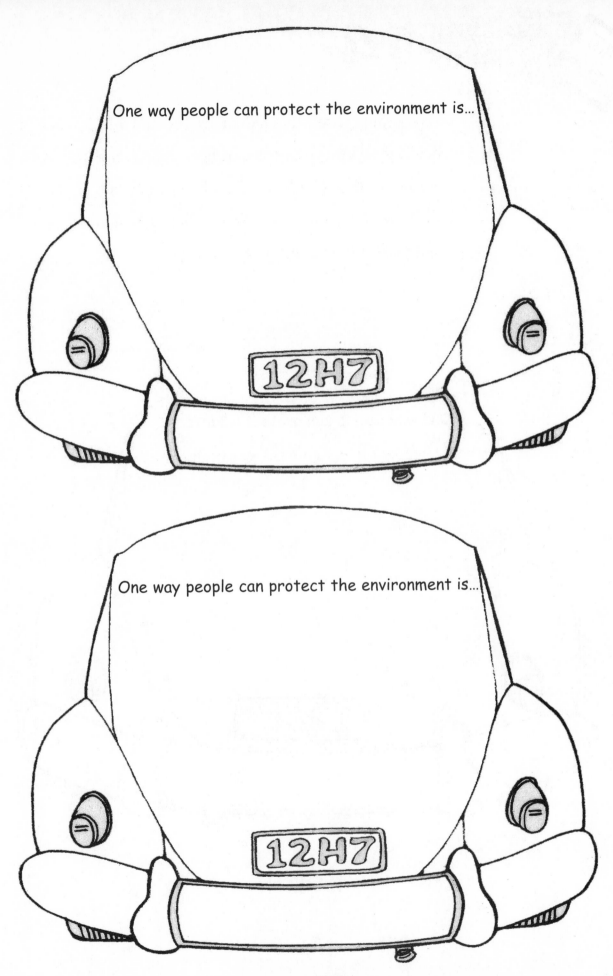

One way people can protect the environment is...

One way people can protect the environment is...

12H7

12H7

113

As a group, carefully read pages 147 and 148 in your
book. Find three examples of how people can protect
wildlife. For each idea, complete the sentence on the car.
Then design a simple bumper sticker that someone who
likes that idea might put on a car.

One way people can protect wildlife is...

12H7

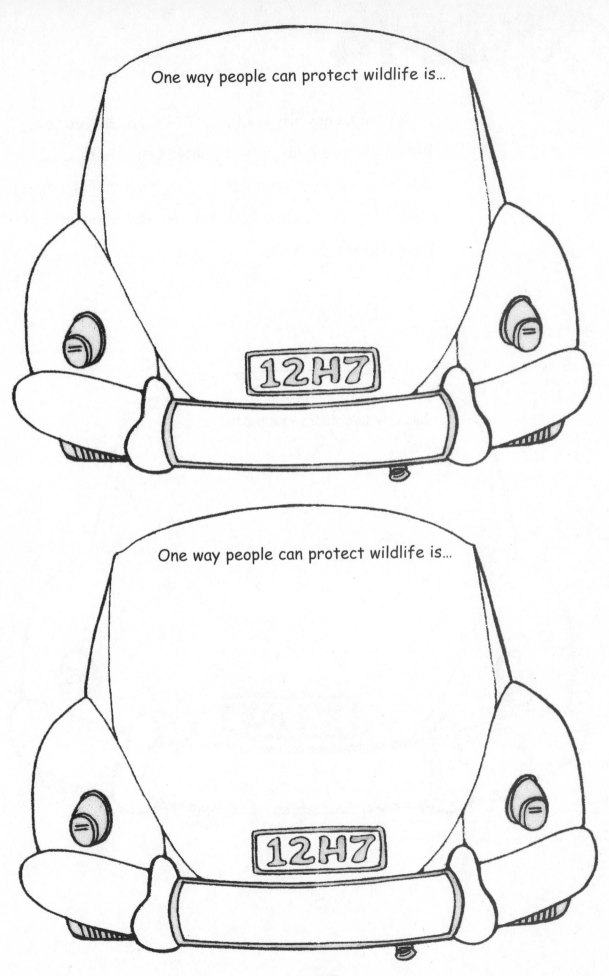

One way people can protect wildlife is...

One way people can protect wildlife is...

As a group, carefully read pages 149–151 in your book. Find three examples of how people can help others. For each idea, complete the sentence on the car. Then design a simple bumper sticker that someone who likes that idea might put on a car.

One way people can help others is...

12H7

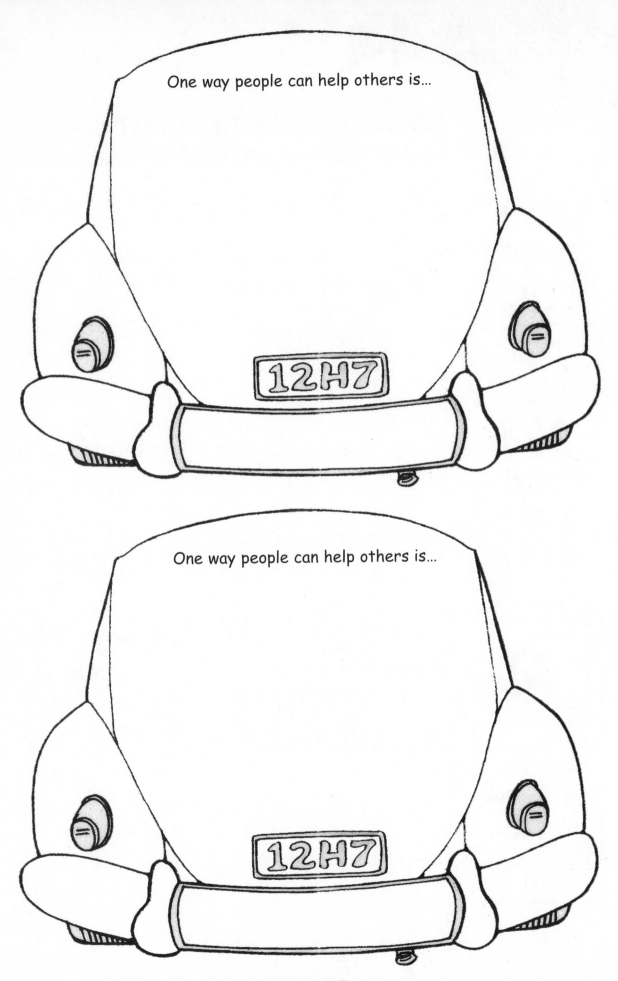

One way people can help others is...

One way people can help others is...

Creating a Proposal for a Class Project

Step 1: Assign the jobs for creating the proposal.

_____ is the Proposal Researcher.

(name of group member)

_____ is the Proposal Writer.

(name of group member)

_____ is the Graphic Artist.

(name of group member)

_____ is the Proposal Presenter.

(name of group member)

Teacher's initials _____

Step 2: Select an idea for a class project.

The Proposal Researcher leads a discussion of possible ideas for a class project to help the global community. Circle your chosen topic below.

- Protecting the environment
- Protecting wildlife
- Helping people

Review project ideas from the class list for the topic you circled. Think of your own ideas, too. The idea you select should be a project that

- will really help the environment, wildlife, or people of some part of the global community.
- the class can realistically complete.
- you and others will be excited about doing.

The Proposal Researcher should write your group's idea for class project here:

Teacher's initials _____

Step 3: Write a first draft of your project proposal. The Proposal Writer leads a discussion of ideas for completing the project proposal. The Proposal Writer takes notes on the outline below.

Class Project Proposal Outline

A. Decide on a short, catchy name for your project.

Example: Food for Friends

Project name: _____

B. Come up with one or two main goals for the project.

Example: Collect 500 cans of food to donate to the local soup kitchen.

Goal 1: _____

_____

Goal 2: _____

_____

C. Create a list of items you will need to do this project.

For example:

1. 25 colorful flyers

2. 4 large boxes

Things we will need for the project:

1. _____ 4. _____

2. _____ 5. _____

3. _____ 6. _____

D. Create an action plan of steps that will need to be completed for this class project. Your project should have from four to eight steps.

Example:

1. *Design a flyer for the project, and make 25 copies on colored paper.*
2. *Get permission to place flyers all around school, and then put them up.*
3. *Put collection boxes out every morning at the front door of school.*

Step 1:

Step 2:

Step 3:

Step 4:

Step 5:

Step 6:

Step 7:

Step 8:

Teacher's initials _____

Step 4: Design a poster to show how your project will help the global community.

The Graphic Artist leads a discussion to brainstorm ideas for a simple, colorful poster to show what the positive outcomes of your project will be. The poster should

• have simple pictures or symbols.

• be colorful.

• include the project name in BIG LETTERS.

The Graphic Artist should sketch the poster below.

Teacher's initials _____

Step 5: Brainstorm ideas for an engaging presentation.
The Proposal Presenter leads a discussion to brainstorm a
one- to two-minute presentation of your project proposal.
Remember, your proposal will be judged on these things:

- Will it really help the environment, wildlife, or people
  of some part of the global community?
- Will it be a project the class can realistically complete?
- Will you and others be excited about doing it?

Your presentation should

- include the name of your project.
- mention the goals of your project.
- describe how the project will help the global
  community. (Use the poster here.)
- be creative, fun, and interesting to watch.

Brainstorm ideas for the most interesting way to present
this information to the class. Write your presentation
ideas here:

Teacher's initials _____

Step 6: Prepare the proposal, poster, and presentation. Get these materials to complete your project proposal and poster:

- a copy of *Student Handout 14.3: Class Project Proposal*
- a sheet of poster board or flip chart paper
- crayons, markers, or paints

The **Proposal Writer** should complete the class project proposal in neat, large letters.

The **Graphic Artist** should work with the **Proposal Researcher** to complete the poster.

The **Proposal Presenter** should prepare any other materials for the presentation and then rehearse it. The presentation must be one to two minutes long.

Teacher's initials_____

Keep a journal of the progress of your class project. After each important step in your project, write a journal entry in a separate notebook. Use the format below to write your journal entries.

Today's date:

What happened in the class project today?

How did you feel about what happened today?

Draw a simple picture to show what happened or how you felt about it.

Credits

Lesson 4

33, Susan Jaekel; **34**, Doug Roy; **35**, Doug Roy; **36**, Doug Roy

Lesson 6

44, upper, DJ Simison; **44, lower**, Doug Roy; **45, upper**, DJ Simison; **45, lower**, Doug Roy; **46, upper**, DJ Simison; **46, lower**, Doug Roy; **47, upper**, DJ Simison; **47, lower**, Doug Roy; **48**, Doug Roy; **49**, Doug Roy; **50**, Doug Roy; **51**, Doug Roy; **52, top**, Doug Roy; **53**, Doug Roy; **54**, Doug Roy

Lesson 8

63, Susan Jaekel; **64**, Susan Jaekel; **65**, Susan Jaekel

Lesson 9

68, Doug Roy

Lesson 10

77, Renata Lohman; **78**, Renata Lohman; **79**, Renata Lohman; **80**, Renata Lohman; **81**, Renata Lohman; **82**, Renata Lohman; **83**, Doug Roy

Lesson 11

86, Len Ebert; **87**, Len Ebert; **88**, Len Ebert; **89**, Len Ebert; **90**, Len Ebert; **91**, Len Ebert; **92**, Len Ebert; **93**, Len Ebert; **94**, Len Ebert

Lesson 12

95, Corbis; **96**, Corbis; **97**, Corbis; **98**, © 2002 Andy Sacks/Getty Images/Stone

Lesson 13

101, Doug Roy; **102**, DJ Simison and Jane McCreary; **104**, DJ Simison and Jane McCreary; **106**, DJ Simison and Jane McCreary

Lesson 14

112, Doug Roy; **113**, Doug Roy; **114**, Doug Roy; **115**, Doug Roy; **116**, Doug Roy; **117**, Doug Roy; **118**, Doug Roy; **119**, Doug Roy; **120**, Doug Roy; **122**, Doug Roy; **123**, Doug Roy; **124**, Doug Roy; **125**, Doug Roy